My Gift from Jesus

Written by DOUGLAS J. LARSON

Illustrated by GARY KAPP

BOOKCRAFT INC.
SALT LAKE CITY, UTAH
1972

3rd Printing, 1975

LITHOGRAPHED IN U.S.A.

PUBLISHERS PRESS
SALT LAKE CITY, UTAH

"When it's all finished, how high will it fly, Grandfather?"

"Pretty high, I think, if we sail it down from the top of that old hill behind the house."

"Boy, I can hardly wait!" exclaimed David, as he carefully lifted the airplane high in the air. "Can Kevin help us fly it, too, Grandfather?"

"Sure, we can all fly it together tomorrow when the paint's dry."

"Gee, Grandpa, you're the greatest!" exclaimed David, "the greatest!"

The next day it seemed as if school would never end, and it was hard for the boys to keep their minds on their work. David kept thinking of that beautiful red airplane. It seemed that was all he could think about. The thought kept pushing everything else out of his mind.

Kevin felt excited, too. He kept looking out of the window at the big white clouds and thinking he could see the airplane flying around and around, almost bumping the clouds.

"It was nice of David and his grandfather to let me help fly the airplane," thought Kevin.

Finally the last school bell rang, and out of the door went Kevin to meet David at the flagpole. He could hardly wait for David to come out of his class. He waited and waited, but David didn't come.

"Maybe he was so excited that he has already gone home," Kevin thought. "I'll just run over to his house and meet him there."

As Kevin came close to David's house he could see that something different was happening. There were lots of cars parked outside, and he could see the bishop and some of the neighbor ladies going in and out of the house.

"Maybe all these people came to watch us fly the airplane," he thought.

Then Kevin noticed someone down by the stream under the old elm tree. It looked like David, and he was crying.

Hurrying over to him, Kevin asked, "What's the matter? Did something happen to the airplane?"

David didn't answer for a moment as he wiped the tears away from his eyes. Then he said: "No...Grandfather died. They say his heart just stopped because he was getting old. I don't think he was so old! He wasn't too old to make airplanes." And at that, David's eyes again began to fill up with big tears.

After a while the two boys walked slowly back to the house and went in the back door. There in its usual place sat Grandfather's old rocking chair. It looked so empty and lonesome just sitting there. David thought his heart was going to burst. He loved his grandfather about as much as anyone in the whole world, and he wondered if he would ever see him again.

That evening David's father called the family together because he had something important to tell them. When they were all quietly seated around the front room, Father began to speak.

"We are all sad and sorrowful about what has happened today and we will all miss Grandfather very much, but I would like to remind each of you of some very important things that will help us feel a little better."

"I don't think I will ever feel better," exclaimed David, wiping a big tear from his eye.

Mother lovingly put her arm around David and hugged him gently.

"We know that before coming to live on this earth," continued Father, "we lived in heaven with our Heavenly Father. We were created by our Heavenly Father as his spirit children. Our elder brother Jesus Christ was there also. Under the direction of our Father in heaven, Jesus created this wonderful earth that we now live on."

"When we were told that we could come and receive earthly bodies for our spirit bodies to live in, we were so happy that we shouted for joy. The Bible tells us that we also sang. Each of us was there—Grandfather and Grandmother were there, also."

"None of us can remember the day that Grandfather left his heavenly home to come to earth, because we were still in heaven.

"Grandfather has often told us that the day he was born it was cold and snowy. His mother told him that. He was born as a tiny baby to your great-grandmother in a little farmhouse that wintry day many years ago."

"Well, Grandfather has had a good life and has been with us for these many years, but today he has left us. Your mother and I were with him when he went. We did not see him go, but we knew the moment he left; for his body quietly gave up its life, and the spirit of Grandfather left its earthly home to go to a new and wonderful life in the spirit world. This is a wonderful and special day for Grandfather. Do you know why?"

"I think I know," answered David. "Is it because Grandfather is now with Grandmother?"

"Yes, David, that's right. Today his spirit body—his spirit, as we call it—has gone on to be with Grandmother and the other loved ones who have gone before him. I am sure he is very happy at this moment, being with so many of his friends again."

"But what about Grandfather's earthly body?" asked David. "Will Grandfather not ever have it again?"

"That's a good question, David," answered Father, "especially since we know how happy we were to be able to receive bodies. Actually, no one would be able to have his earthly body again after he dies if it were not for our Savior Jesus Christ."

"Remember, Jesus too came to the earth from his Father in heaven to receive an earthly body. He was born to his mother Mary. He came to earth to be our Savior."

"Jesus had a great work to do here on earth. When he was grown he went about his work, teaching people and explaining to them the things they must do in order to be able to return to heaven and live again with our Heavenly Father."

"But there were many who would not believe Jesus and would not accept the Church which he had established. Some of these men placed him on the cross and crucified him. The Bible tells us that when he died he gave up the spirit. In other words, his spirit left his body and went to the spirit world, the world where spirits live."

"A good man named Joseph took Jesus' body down from the cross and placed it in a tomb, where a large stone was rolled in front of the opening so that no one could enter."

"On the third day Jesus' spirit returned from the spirit world where it had been during the three days that his body lay in the tomb. This spirit or spirit body came again into Jesus' earthly body and raised it from the dead—resurrected it. In other words, his earthly body became alive again because the spirit body returned to it to give it life."

"Shortly after Jesus was resurrected he appeared to his apostles who were meeting together in an upper room of a house. The Bible tells us that at first the apostles were surprised and frightened, for they had never seen a resurrected person. Jesus invited each of them to feel his hands and body so that they would know for themselves that he was not just a spirit but had a resurrected body of flesh and bones. Coming forward one by one, each apostle felt the hands and body of their Savior and knew that he had truly been resurrected."

"Jesus was the first person ever to be resurrected. His resurrection brought resurrection to all people who have died or will die. This is a gift Jesus gives to each of us. Someday Grandfather's spirit body will return from the spirit world and will be joined again with his earthly body, and he will be resurrected. Everyone who has ever lived on this earth will someday be resurrected, and then they will never die again."

As David sat in the church attending the funeral services for his grandfather, he had a warm and happy feeling in his heart. He had this feeling not just because so many people had so many good things to say about his grandfather, nor because of all the kind things the neighbors had done for his family, but because he knew that Grandfather was truly alive in the spirit world. Someday David would see his grandfather again. Especially was he happy and grateful to Jesus, who had provided the way for Grandfather's body to be raised from the grave.

David thought: "Truly Jesus is our Savior, because he has saved our bodies from the grave. What a wonderful day it will be for Grandfather when he returns to receive his body again in the resurrection!"

"Look at her fly!" shouted David, as the plane rose high
into the air as if it would fly up to heaven. "Grandfather would
sure be proud of it if he could see it now."

"He sure would!" exclaimed Kevin, "he sure would!"

Here Are Some of the Important Things We Have Learned

1. Each spirit or spirit body came to earth to receive an earthly body.

2. The time that the spirit leaves the body is known as death.

3. After life here on earth, our spirits go on to a place called the spirit world.

4. In the spirit world we will be able to be together again with our loved ones who have died, and that will be a happy time for us.

5. The resurrection is the time when our spirit body is joined again with our earthly body, which will never die again.

6. One way that Jesus is our Savior is through the resurrection.

7. Because Jesus Christ was resurrected from the grave, he has provided the way for all of us to someday be resurrected.